Other books by Bill Stott, published by Exley Publications:
The Crazy World of Cats
The Crazy World of Gardening
The Crazy World of Hospitals
The Crazy World of Music
The Crazy World of Photography
The Crazy World of Rugby
After-Dinner Jokes
Business Jokes
Golf Jokes
Naughty Jokes.

The Illustrated Motoring Address Book

MOTORIST'S
LOG BOOK

🔲EXLEY

A copy of the CIP is available from the British Library on request.

ISBN: 1-85015-280-2

First published in Great Britain in 1991 by Exley Publications.
Published simultaneously in 1993 by Exley Giftbooks, 232 Madison Avenue, Suite 1206, NY 10016, USA and Exley Publications Ltd, 16 Chalk Hill, Watford, Herts WD1 4BN.
Reprinted 1992 (twice), 1993.
Fifth printing 1994

Editor: Helen Exley
Cartoons: Bill Stott
Words: Margaret Montgomery
Designed by the Pinpoint Design Company

Exley Publications and Bill Stott would like to thank *Auto-Express* for permission to use the cartoons in this book.

Printed in Hungary.

MOTORIST'S
LOG BOOK

Bill Stott

⬚EXLEY

INTRODUCTION

The Motorist's Logbook is a useful accessory for any motoring enthusiast. With simple checks to ensure your vehicle is running smoothly, information on what to do in the event of a breakdown or accident, pages to keep personal details, service records, telephone numbers and notes, this book will help to keep your motoring as trouble free as possible.

CONTENTS

"THAT'S RIGHT — ONE OWNER. IT'S BE NICKED A FEW TIMES
BUT IT'S ONLY EVER HAD ONE OWNER —"

Vehicle Details

MAKE	Renault			
MODEL	S agrane	COLOUR	white	
YEAR OF REGISTRATION				
REGISTRATION NUMBER	EL 799 QTP			
ENGINE NUMBER				
CHASSIS/VIN NUMBER				
FUEL TANK CAPACITY		TYPE OF FUEL	unleaded	
ENGINE OIL CAPACITY				
COOLING SYSTEM CAPACITY				
GEARBOX CAPACITY				
TYRE SIZE				
RECOMMENDED SPARK PLUGS				
SPARK PLUG GAP				
CONTACT BREAKER GAP				
VALVE CLEARANCES	Inlet	hot: cold:	Exhaust	hot: cold:

Personal Reminders

INSURANCE COMPANY			
ADDRESS			
		TELEPHONE NUMBER	
INSURANCE POLICY NUMBER		RENEWAL DATE	
TYPE OF COVER			
MOTORING ORGANIZATION			
MEMBERSHIP NUMBER		RENEWAL DATE	
EMERGENCY TELEPHONE NUMBER			
DRIVING LICENCE NUMBER			
ROAD FUND LICENCE RENEWAL DATE			
MOT RENEWAL DATE			

Emergency Checklist

The following items should be kept in your vehicle in case of emergencies.

BULBS		POLYTHENE SHEETING	
EMERGENCY WINDSCREEN		RAGS	
FAN BELT		SOCKET SET	
FIRE EXTINGUISHER		SPARE WHEEL	
FIRST AID EMERGENCY BOOKLET		STRING	
FIRST AID SET		TOOL KIT	
FUEL CAN		TORCH	
FUSES		TOW ROPE	
INSURANCE CERTIFICATE		WARNING TRIANGLE	
JACK AND WHEELBRACE		WATER CONTAINER	
JUMP LEADS		WHEEL LOCKING NUT KEY	
LOOSE CHANGE		WIRE	
MOTORING ORGANIZATION MEMBERSHIP CARD			

Maintenance

To avoid unnecessary breakdowns, have your vehicle serviced regularly and carry out the following maintenance items yourself.

DAILY

Clean the windscreen and make sure the wipers work.

Clean and check the lights and indicators. Replace any broken bulbs.

Check the condition of the tyres.

Clean the mirrors.

Maintenance

Check tyre pressures and depth of tread. Don't forget the spare.

Check the level of the clutch and brake fluid and, if necessary, top up. Check the reservoirs for leaks.

Check the level of the engine oil and, if necessary, top up.

Check the level of the battery fluid and, if necessary, top up with distilled water.

Check the level of the engine coolant and, if necessary, top up.

Check that the windscreen wiper blades are in good condition.

Check and, if necessary, top up the windscreen washer fluid.

Check the tension of the fan belt and look for signs of wear.

Check rubber hoses and pipes for leaks.

Useful Conversions

FUEL	
Gallons to litres	multiply by 4.55
Litres to gallons	multiply by 0.22
Pounds per gallon to pence per litre	multiply by 22
Pence per litre to pounds per gallon	multiply by 0.0455
SPEED	
Miles per hour to kilometres per hour	multiply by 1.61
Kilometres per hour to miles per hour	multiply by 0.62
TYRE PRESSURES	
Pounds per square inch to kilograms per square centimetre	multiply by 0.07
Kilograms per square centimetre to pounds per square inch	multiply by 14.2
WEIGHT	
Pounds to kilograms	multiply by 0.45
Kilograms to pounds	multiply by 2.20

"BAD NEWS, I'M AFRAID... AS YOU CAN SEE, THE SHORT NIGGLY BLACK THING'S COME ADRIFT FROM THE ERM AND I THINK THE GREENISH-BROWN DOO-DAH MAY BE BURNED OUT...."

How to use the Fuel Consumption Record

Make a note of your mileage every time you fill up, then work out how many miles per gallon your vehicle does. Check this figure against the manufacturer's specification to see if the engine is correctly tuned, or if it needs adjusting. Use the comments column to note business mileage. This will be vital when making expenses claims and completing tax returns.

Date	Mileage	Fuel Gallons/Litres	Price Per Gal/Litre	Brought forward £15.00	Comments and Business/Personal Mileage Record
3 Jan	2062	7g	2.37/g	£31.59	Trade fair 96 miles
10 Jan	2158	—	—	—	Sales Conference 8 miles
12 Jan	2166	2g	2.40/g	£36.39	Seminar 78 miles
					Health Club 5 miles
14 Jan	2249	—	—	—	Shopping 4 miles
					Cinema 8 miles
					Squash + supper 30 miles
					Visit to Roger + Sue 50 miles
16 Jan	2341	—	—	—	Kids to Brownies 6 miles
17 Jan	2347	4g	2.42/g	£46.07	Sales Conference 150 miles

Fuel Consumption Record

Brought forward

Date	Mileage	Fuel Gallons/Litres	Price Per Gal/Litre		Comments and Business/Personal Mileage Record
16.8.96	26313	—	—	—	Home 160 miles
17.8.96	26973	—	—	—	Clevelys 10 miles
18.8.96	26983	—	—	—	Morrisons 10 miles
	26984	—	—	—	B and Q 6 miles
	26984				
7.11.97 87900		—	—		
		PAGE TOTAL			

19

Fuel Consumption Record

Brought forward

Date	Mileage	Fuel Gallons/Litres	Price Per Gal/Litre		Comments and Business/Personal Mileage Record
10 Aug	50240	60.0	3 3	20.00	Preston 30 Miles
11	50320	—	—	—	Morrisons 10 miles
11	50330	—	—	—	Swimming 5 miles
12 Aug	50335	—	—	Loncan	Windermere 64
11	50347	—	—	—	Windermere Irale
11	50348	—	—	—	Home 5 miles
12	50462	—	—	—	Morrisons 10 mly
13 Aug	50472	—	—	—	Post office 1 Mile
11	50473	—	—	—	B+Q 3 miles
11	50476	—	—	—	Home 4 miles
11	50480	—	—	—	Cleveleys 6 miles
11	50086	—	—	—	B+Q 2 miles
11	50488	—	—	—	Home 4 miles
			PAGE TOTAL	20.00	202 miles

Fuel Consumption Record

Date	Mileage	Fuel Gallons/Litres	Price Per Gal/Litre		Comments and Business/Personal Mileage Record
26th	50692	66.8		42.00	Tesco. 3 miles
11	50695		60.4		Home 3 miles
1.1	50698				Garden Centre, 5.5
1.1	50504				Home 5.5 miles
25th		50510			Colne
11					Home
		PAGE TOTAL			

21

Fuel Consumption Record

Brought forward

Date	Mileage	Fuel Gallons/Litres	Price Per Gal/Litre		Comments and Business/Personal Mileage Record
			PAGE TOTAL		

22

Fuel Consumption Record

Brought forward

Date	Mileage	Fuel Gallons/Litres	Price Per Gal/Litre		Comments and Business/Personal Mileage Record
			PAGE TOTAL		

"IF WE DON'T KNOW ANYBODY IN A BIG ORANGE TRUCK, WHY IS HE WAVING AT US?"

Fuel Consumption Record

Date	Mileage	Fuel Gallons/Litres	Price Per Gal/Litre		Comments and Business/Personal Mileage Record
			PAGE TOTAL		

Fuel Consumption Record

Date	Mileage	Fuel Gallons/Litres	Price Per Gal/Litre	Brought forward	Comments and Business/Personal Mileage Record
			PAGE TOTAL		

Fuel Consumption Record

Date	Mileage	Fuel Gallons/Litres	Price Per Gal/Litre		Comments and Business/Personal Mileage Record
			PAGE TOTAL		

Fuel Consumption Record

Brought forward

Date	Mileage	Fuel Gallons/Litres	Price Per Gal/Litre		Comments and Business/Personal Mileage Record
			PAGE TOTAL		

"WHAT'S 'TOP HOSE' IN SERBO-CROAT?"

Fuel Consumption Record

Brought forward

Date	Mileage	Fuel Gallons/Litres	Price Per Gal/Litre		Comments and Business/Personal Mileage Record
			PAGE TOTAL		

Fuel Consumption Record

Date	Mileage	Fuel Gallons/Litres	Price Per Gal/Litre	Brought forward	Comments and Business/Personal Mileage Record
			PAGE TOTAL		

Fuel Consumption Record

Brought forward

Date	Mileage	Fuel Gallons/Litres	Price Per Gal/Litre		Comments and Business/Personal Mileage Record
			PAGE TOTAL		

"STEREO'S NOT TOO LOUD, GRANDAD?"

Fuel Consumption Record

Date	Mileage	Fuel Gallons/Litres	Price Per Gal/Litre		Comments and Business/Personal Mileage Record
			PAGE TOTAL		

Fuel Consumption Record

Brought forward

Date	Mileage	Fuel Gallons/Litres	Price Per Gal/Litre		Comments and Business/Personal Mileage Record
			PAGE TOTAL		

Fuel Consumption Record

Brought forward

Date	Mileage	Fuel Gallons/Litres	Price Per Gal/Litre		Comments and Business/Personal Mileage Record
			PAGE TOTAL		

Fuel Consumption Record

Date	Mileage	Fuel Gallons/Litres	Price Per Gal/Litre		Comments and Business/Personal Mileage Record
			PAGE TOTAL		

Fuel Consumption Record

Brought forward

Date	Mileage	Fuel Gallons/Litres	Price Per Gal/Litre		Comments and Business/Personal Mileage Record
			PAGE TOTAL		

Fuel Consumption Record

Date	Mileage	Fuel Gallons/Litres	Price Per Gal/Litre		Comments and Business/Personal Mileage Record
			PAGE TOTAL		

"ARE YOU CONVERSANT WITH THE HAND SIGNALS YOUR CHILDREN HAVE BEEN MAKING AT ME FOR THE PAST TEN MILES?"

Fuel Consumption Record

Brought forward

Date	Mileage	Fuel Gallons/Litres	Price Per Gal/Litre		Comments and Business/Personal Mileage Record
			PAGE TOTAL		

Fuel Consumption Record

Date	Mileage	Fuel Gallons/Litres	Price Per Gal/Litre	Brought forward	Comments and Business/Personal Mileage Record
			PAGE TOTAL		

Fuel Consumption Record

Date	Mileage	Fuel Gallons/Litres	Price Per Gal/Litre		Comments and Business/Personal Mileage Record
			PAGE TOTAL		

43

Fuel Consumption Record

Date	Mileage	Fuel Gallons/Litres	Price Per Gal/Litre		Comments and Business/Personal Mileage Record
			PAGE TOTAL		

"YOU HEAR A FUNNY NOISE THEN?"

Fuel Consumption Record

Date	Mileage	Fuel Gallons/Litres	Price Per Gal/Litre		Comments and Business/Personal Mileage Record
			PAGE TOTAL		

Fuel Consumption Record

Brought forward

Date	Mileage	Fuel Gallons/Litres	Price Per Gal/Litre		Comments and Business/Personal Mileage Record
			PAGE TOTAL		

Fuel Consumption Record

Brought forward

Date	Mileage	Fuel Gallons/Litres	Price Per Gal/Litre		Comments and Business/Personal Mileage Record
			PAGE TOTAL		

Fuel Consumption Record

Brought forward

Date	Mileage	Fuel Gallons/Litres	Price Per Gal/Litre		Comments and Business/Personal Mileage Record
			PAGE TOTAL		

Fuel Consumption Record

Brought forward

Date	Mileage	Fuel Gallons/Litres	Price Per Gal/Litre		Comments and Business/Personal Mileage Record
			PAGE TOTAL		

"THIS IS MY HUSBAND BARRY. BARRY DOES ALL HIS OWN SERVICING...."

Fuel Consumption Record

Date	Mileage	Fuel Gallons/Litres	Price Per Gal/Litre		Comments and Business/Personal Mileage Record
			PAGE TOTAL		

52

Fuel Consumption Record

Date	Mileage	Fuel Gallons/Litres	Price Per Gal/Litre	Brought forward	Comments and Business/Personal Mileage Record
			PAGE TOTAL		

Breakdown Procedure

On a busy road or on the hard shoulder of a motorway, always use the nearside door to get out of your vehicle – do not use the driver's door. Passengers should also use the nearside doors to get out.

If possible, get your vehicle off the road or in a safe position.

Warn other road users that there is an obstruction. Turn on the hazard warning lights and place a warning triangle 50 metres behind the vehicle (150 metres on a motorway hard shoulder).

At night or if visibility is poor, leave the side lights on and make sure the rear hazard warning lights are not obscured.

If you need assistance from a motoring organization, find the nearest telephone and call the organization's emergency number. On a motorway, follow the direction of the arrows on marker posts to the nearest SOS telephone. The police will pass your details on to the relevant organization. You will need to give the following information:

    the registration number of your vehicle
    the make, model and colour of your vehicle
    your membership number
    the location of the vehicle

details of the breakdown
the telephone number you are calling from

Wait for assistance to arrive in a safe place off the road or on the hard shoulder of the motorway. Do not let passengers, especially children, wander about.

Emergency Telephone Numbers

MOTORING ORGANIZATION	
BREAKDOWN RECOVERY SERVICE	
MOBILE WINDSCREEN SERVICE	
LOCAL GARAGE	
MOBILE MECHANIC	

Accident Procedure

If you are involved in an accident, stop your vehicle and turn off the engine.

Switch on the hazard warning lights, if they are still working, and use a warning triangle to let other road users know that there has been an accident.

Exchange the following details with the other party/parties:

    name and address of driver and owner, if different
    make and type of vehicle
    registration number
    insurance company
    policy number

Make a note of the damage to your vehicle, other vehicles involved and surrounding property.

Take the name, address and telephone number of any independent witnesses.

Make a note of the date and time of the accident, where it happened, the weather, road conditions, visibility, number of people injured and any other relevant details.

Take photographs of the scene, if you have a camera.

If anyone is injured, you *must* call the police. Give them as many details as you can – where the accident happened, the number of vehicles involved, the number of casualties, any hazards. The police will call the other emergency services.

Do not move any casualties, unless they are in further danger – wait for medical help.

Motor Accident Report

DATE		PLACE			TIME	
DETAILS OF OTHER VEHICLE						
Make and Model			Colour			
Registration Number						
Name and address of driver						
			Telephone number			
Name and address of owner (if different)						
			Telephone number			
Name and address of insurance company						
			Telephone number			
Policy number			Renewal date			
DETAILS OF INDEPENDENT WITNESSES						
Name						
Address						
			Telephone number			

Name	
Address	

		Telephone number	

CASUALTIES			
Name and address			
Injury sustained			Wearing seat belt YES / NO
Name and address			
Injury sustained			Wearing seat belt YES / NO

OTHER DETAILS			
Weather		Visibility	
Road conditions			
Names and numbers of police officers, if present			

Tyre Maintenance

Check the condition of the tyres every day. Look for cuts and uneven wear, and remove any nails or stones.

Check the tread wear of all the tyres, including the spare. Measure the depth of the tread at different points across the width of the tyre. In the United Kingdom, the legal requirement is one millimetre, but ideally the tyres should have at least two or three millimetres of tread.

Tyre pressures should be checked every week and always before starting a long journey. Don't forget to check the spare as well. Tyres that are not correctly inflated can affect the steering, tread wear, fuel economy and comfort.

Check the pressure when the tyres are cold.

Tyre pressures are usually measured in pounds per square inch or kilograms per square centimetre. Make a note below of the recommended tyre size and tyre pressures for your vehicle.

TYRE SIZE:				
	NORMAL		FULLY LADEN	
Tyre Pressures:	Front	Rear	Front	Rear

Maintenance and Service forms

Use the maintenance and service forms to keep a record of everything you spend on the upkeep of your vehicle.

Whenever you replace a worn-out item, have the vehicle serviced at the garage, have repairs done or do them yourself, or buy accessories, write down the details.

You will be able to see how reliable the vehicle has been, how well you have maintained it and how much it all cost. If you decide to sell the vehicle, you'll have a detailed record to show potential buyers.

"HEAR THAT? THE EEK-EEK-EEK HAS GONE BUT NOW THERE'S A DISTINCT THUM-THUM-THUM...."

Repairs and Services

Date	Mileage	Service: Description of Work	Labour	Parts	

Repairs and Services

Date	Mileage	Service: Description of Work	Labour	Parts	

Repairs and Services

Date	Mileage	Service: Description of Work	Labour	Parts	

Repairs and Services

Date	Mileage	Service: Description of Work	Labour	Parts	

MANIFOLD GARAGE
WHEEL BALANCING A SPECIALITY

Repairs and Services

Date	Mileage	Service: Description of Work	Labour	Parts	

Repairs and Services

Date	Mileage	Service: Description of Work	Labour	Parts	

Repairs and Services

Date	Mileage	Service: Description of Work	Labour	Parts	

"BE REASONABLE DAD — WHAT'S MORE IMPORTANT — A LUXURY FULLY INSURED COMPANY CAR, OR THE POOR LITTLE SQUIRREL WE SWERVED TO AVOID?"

Repairs and Services

Date	Mileage	Service: Description of Work	Labour	Parts	

Repairs and Services

Date	Mileage	Service: Description of Work	Labour	Parts	

Other Expenses

Date	Oil	Parking	Garaging	Car Wash	Brought forward	Comments
				PAGE TOTAL		

Other Expenses

Date	Oil	Parking	Garaging	Car Wash	Brought forward	Comments
				PAGE TOTAL		

Other Expenses

Date	Oil	Parking	Garaging	Car Wash	Brought forward	Comments
				PAGE TOTAL		

Other Expenses

Brought forward

Date	Oil	Parking	Garaging	Car Wash		Comments
				PAGE TOTAL		

"IT'S TRUE WHAT THEY SAY ABOUT ABS BRAKES – THEY DIDN'T LOCK UP AT ALL BEFORE I HIT YOU."

Other Expenses

Brought forward

Date	Oil	Parking	Garaging	Car Wash		Comments
				PAGE TOTAL		

Other Expenses

Date	Oil	Parking	Garaging	Car Wash	Brought forward	Comments
				PAGE TOTAL		

Other Expenses

Date	Oil	Parking	Garaging	Car Wash		Comments
				PAGE TOTAL		

Annual Expenses

	Year		Year		Comments
Motor Tax					
Insurance					
Garaging					
Depreciation					
Subscription fees					
Other					
	YEAR TOTAL		YEAR TOTAL		

80

Summary of Costs

	Year		Year		Comments
Fuel					
Repairs and Services					
Other Expenses					
Yearly Expenses					

With your yearly expense total and yearly mileage, you can calculate your motoring cost per mile.

Notes

"THERE! I KNEW I WAS RIGHT! — 'THE SPLIT REAR SEAT OPTION IS ONLY AVAILABLE ON LX AND EXi MODELS....'"

Notes

Notes

Notes

Notes

Notes

Notes

Notes

"WELL, HIS SPANISH IS HARDLY TEXT BOOK,
BUT APPARENTLY WE'VE RUN OVER HIS TACO STAND...."

Telephone Numbers

Name	Number	Name	Number

Telephone Numbers

Name	Number	Name	Number